LEARN AS YOU PLAY TUBA

BY PETER WASTALL

Revised edition 1990

Learn As You Play is a series of instrumental tutors designed
specifically to prepare pupils for the early grades of all
the principal examination boards. The tutors are suitable
for both E♭ and B♭ tuba.

The course, places the maximum emphasis on the
early development of musicianship. From the
beginning it introduces the student to a wide
range of music, including works by leading
contemporary composers. Each unit contains
the following teaching programme:

1

New material is presented in clear progressive steps

2

Short, concise exercises enable new skills
to be quickly developed

3

Instrumental solos by distinguished composers
stimulate and develop practice repertoire

4

Progressive technical studies gradually bring the student
into contact with specific instrumental technique

5

Instrumental duets (alternate units) provide experience
in ensemble playing. Keyboard accompaniments
to the duets can be added in early units

Progress is measured by the introduction
of Concert Pieces which utilise all
previously learned material

Piano accompaniments are available for these pieces
in a separate accompaniment book. The Concert Pieces
are works representative of examination requirements
and in many instances are works which have been set
in current or past syllabuses.

SERIES EDITOR
PETER WASTALL

BOOSEY & HAWKES

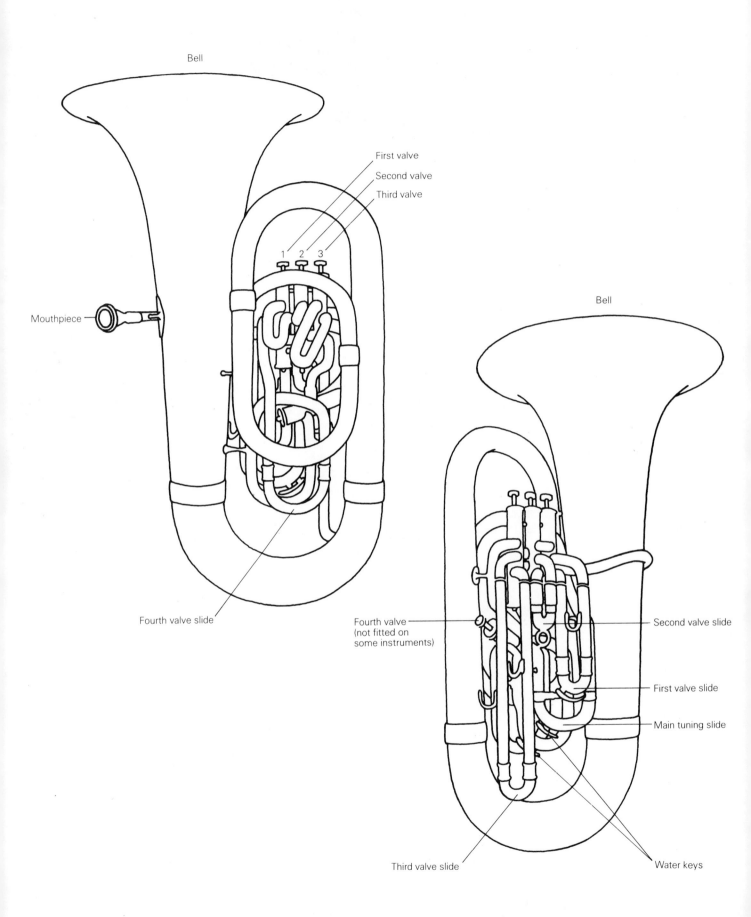

Bell

First valve

Second valve

Third valve

1   2   3

Mouthpiece

Fourth valve slide

Bell

Fourth valve
(not fitted on
some instruments)

Second valve slide

First valve slide

Main tuning slide

Third valve slide

Water keys

The instrument illustrated is a Besson "Sovereign"
E♭ fully-compensating 4-valved tuba (Models 981/982).

Playing position

Usually, the tuba rests on the player's thighs, the left hand giving additional support. The right hand fingertips are positioned over the valves.

Left hand position

When a fourth valve is fitted the left hand fingers are positioned over the fourth valve ready to depress it when required (units 12–20).

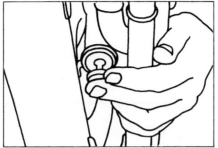

Mouthpiece placement

The mouthpiece is usually placed centrally on the lips, with two thirds of the top lip and one third of the bottom lip showing inside the mouthpiece when a visualiser is used.

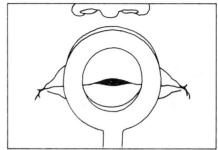

Open notes – E♭ tuba

In keeping with other brass instruments, the E♭ tuba has a range of notes that can be produced without depressing any of the valves. After producing the initial 'buzz', try to produce one of these open notes, starting on whichever is most comfortable to play. Usually a pupil's first notes are either E♭, B♭ or low E♭. The main objective will be to play B♭. If the first notes are higher than B♭, relax the muscles at the lip centre. If the first notes are lower than B♭, firm the muscles around the aperture. Once the B♭ is established, relax down to the low E♭ and compare the embouchure formation required to play these two basic sounds.

After experimenting with the open notes, compare the sounds of B♭, A♭, G, F and E♭.

Open notes – B♭ tuba

In keeping with other brass instruments, the B♭ tuba has a range of notes that can be produced without depressing any of the valves. After producing the initial 'buzz', try to produce one of these open notes, starting on whichever is most comfortable to play. Usually a pupil's first notes are either B♭, F or low B♭. The main objective will be to play the upper of the two B♭s. If the first notes are higher than the upper B♭, relax the muscles at the lip centre. If the first notes are lower than the upper B♭, firm the muscles around the aperture. Once the upper B♭ is established, relax down to the F and compare the embouchure required to play these two basic sounds.

Try to start each note with a tongue movement similar to that used when pronouncing the letter 'T'.

Points to remember

1. Hold the mouthpiece lightly against the lips with just enough pressure to stop air escaping.
2. Never allow the cheeks to balloon outwards.
3. Position the jaw so that the lips can vibrate freely.
4. Sit up, with the back straight enabling full deep breaths to be taken.

When tonguing, the tongue should strike the point where the upper teeth and gums meet.

Tuba pitch

When notated in bass clef, tubas are concert pitch instruments and all read from the same part regardless of whether their open notes are pitched on an E♭ series or a B♭ series. Pupils using a piano to check pitch should play B♭ a ninth below middle C to establish open B♭ on the tuba.

	B♭	A♭	G	F	E♭
E♭	Open	1	1 2	1 3	Open
B♭	Open	1	1 2	Open	1

PREPARATORY MATERIAL FOR UNIT 1

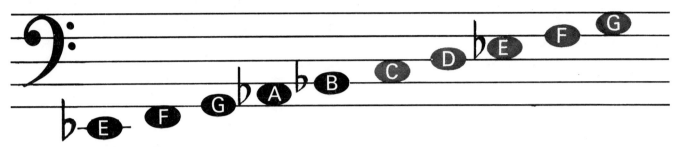

These are the notes shown in the fingering chart

Notation

Printed notes are also named after the first seven letters of the alphabet. From the example it can be seen that they are placed on a staff (the name of the five lines), each line and each space counting as one letter name.

Every note in music can be raised or lowered half a tone. The sign for lowering a note half a tone is the flat sign shown in the example. During units 1 and 2, flat signs will be used to show B♭, A♭ and E♭.

The Bass Clef

Since the same seven letter names are used for all instruments (i.e. those that produce high notes, as well as those that produce low notes) a clef sign is placed at the beginning of each staff to establish exact pitch. Except in brass bands, tuba music is written in bass clef.

Note Lengths

The length of time a note is played is measured by the beat; the difference in length being shown by various types of note. The three types used in unit 1 are:

Play the following crotchets trying to hold each for exactly the same amount of time.

Now play the following minims, holding each note for the whole of beats one and two added together.

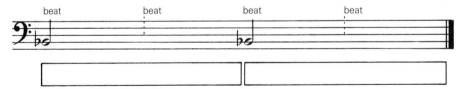

Now play a semibreve, trying to hold the note for exactly four beats.

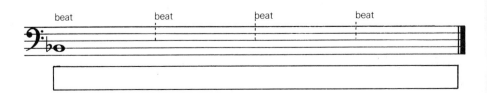

4

Bars and bar lines

Bar line   Double bar line

Beats usually group themselves into regular patterns of either two, three or four; to show these patterns, the music is divided by bar lines into bars.

A double bar-line is used to separate differing sections of music within a single piece.

A thin/thick double bar indicates the end of a piece or exercise.

Time Signatures

A time-signature is placed at the beginning of each piece of music to show how many beats there are in a bar, and the type of note that equals one beat. It is printed in a fractional form, the value of the crotchet being shown as a fraction of a semibreve.

$\frac{2}{4}$ showing 2 crotchet beats in each bar

$\frac{3}{4}$ showing 3 crotchet beats in each bar

$\frac{4}{4}$ showing 4 crotchet beats in each bar

UNIT 1

Flat Signs (summarised from p.4)

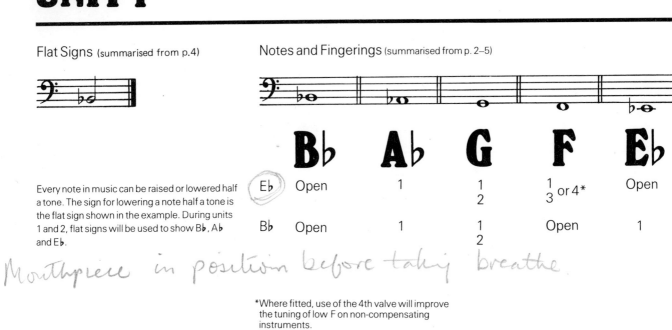

Every note in music can be raised or lowered half a tone. The sign for lowering a note half a tone is the flat sign shown in the example. During units 1 and 2, flat signs will be used to show B♭, A♭ and E♭.

Notes and Fingerings (summarised from p. 2–5)

	B♭	A♭	G	F	E♭
E♭	Open	1	1 2	1 3 or 4*	Open
B♭	Open	1	1 2	Open	1

Mouthpiece in position before taking breathe

*Where fitted, use of the 4th valve will improve the tuning of low F on non-compensating instruments.

Exercise 1

Exercise 2

Exercise 3

Exercise 4

Exercise 5

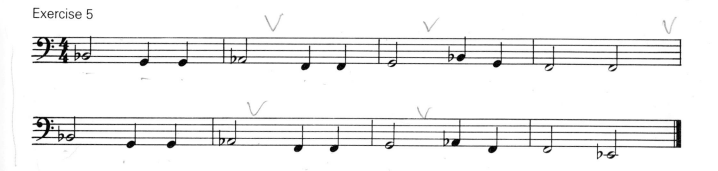

Musicianship

When you practise the instrumental solos, notice how the notes form patterns almost as if they were words in a rhyme. In music these note patterns are called phrases; to help to identify them, phrases in some early pieces have been marked with brackets. Breaths are normally taken at the ends of phrases; additional breaths can be taken, but these must be discreet so as not to disturb the natural flow of the phrase.

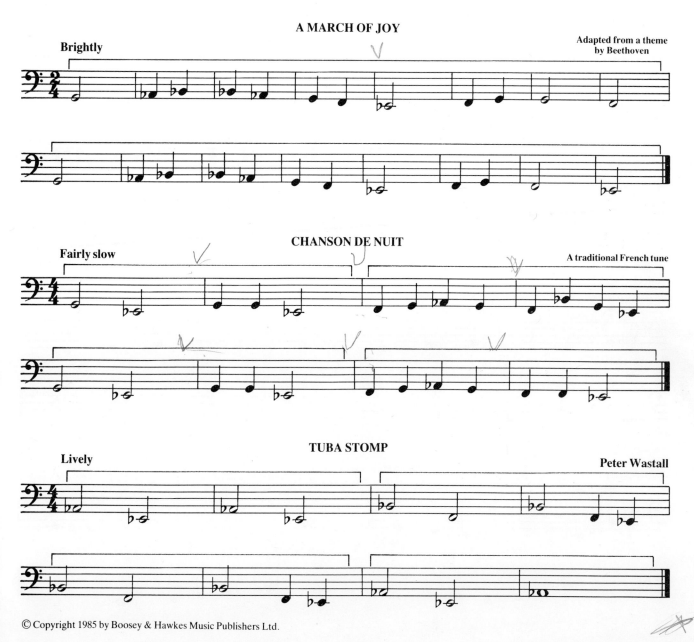

UNIT 2

The Pause Sign

27/9/93

Rests

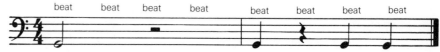

When a pause sign is placed over a note, the beat stops and the note is played for a period of time longer than its printed value. During the first section of this book the pause will be used mainly in the exercises, identifying individual notes that are to be sustained for as long as possible.

The length of time in which notes are not played is shown by various rests, each note having an equivalent rest. The example shows the minim rest (two beats of silence) and the crotchet rest (one beat of silence).

4/10/93

FFIGYSBREN

At a moderate speed

A traditional Welsh tune

Tone development

One of the best ways to develop a full tone is to play individual long notes. In the exercise that follows, carry out the following drill:

1. Listen closely to the sound, aiming for a full, even tone.

2. Check that the diaphragm is giving a firm support to the air stream.

3. Check that the instrument is held in such a position that the lips can vibrate freely.

LET'S BEGUINE
(A duet for pupil and teacher)

In the style of a beguine

Peter Wastall

*Chord symbols for keyboard accompaniment.

9

UNIT 3

Eb TUBA

New Notes

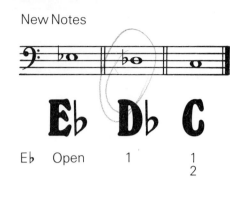

Eb   Open   1   1
                    2

Keys and Key-signatures

*Because of the key signature, both these notes must be played as Eb.

When flat signs are placed at the beginning of each staff they are called a key-signature. Each flat is placed on a specific line or space indicating that every note with that letter name is to be played as if the flat were against the note. The two keys that use the key-signature with four flats are: Ab Major and F Minor.

Dotted Minims

A dot after a note lengthens that note by half its value. Because of this, a dotted minim will be equal to a minim (2 beats) plus half a minim (1 beat), making a total of three crotchet beats.

18/10/93

Ab Major

Exercise 1

Exercise 2

Exercise 3

ABERDEEN

At a moderate speed

An 18th century Scottish melody

11/10/93.

Tone development

1. Use exercise (a) for comparing the embouchure formation for playing open notes Eb–Bb–Eb.
2. Play each note with a strong air pressure, keeping the diaphragm moderately firm.
3. Encourage the lips to vibrate freely, but keep the corners of the mouth in their correct position at all times.
4. Repeat the drill for each exercise.

A LITTLE ETUDE

Fairly slow

Antonio Diabelli

MARCH

Brightly

Nicholas Chédeville

New Notes

D   **C**   **B♭**

| B♭ | 1
2 | 1
3 or 4* | Open |

*Where fitted, use of the 4th valve will improve the tuning of low C on non-compensating instruments.

Keys and Key-signatures

*Because of the key signature, both these notes must be played as B♭.

When flat signs are placed at the beginning of each staff they are called a key-signature. Each flat is placed on a specific line or space indicating that every note with that letter name is to be played as if the flat were against the note. The two keys that use the key-signature with three flats are: E♭ Major and C Minor.

Dotted Minims

beat   beat   beat

A dot after a note lengthens that note by half its value. Because of this, a dotted minim will be equal to a minim (2 beats) plus half a minim (1 beat), making a total of three crotchet beats.

E♭ Major

Exercise 1

Exercise 2

Exercise 3

ABERDEEN

At a moderate speed

An 18th century Scottish melody

Tone development

1. Use exercise (a) for comparing the embouchure formation for playing open notes Bb–F–Bb
2. Play each note with a strong air pressure, keeping the diaphragm moderately firm.

3. Encourage the lips to vibrate freely, but keep the corners of the mouth in their correct position at all times.
4. Repeat the drill for each exercise.

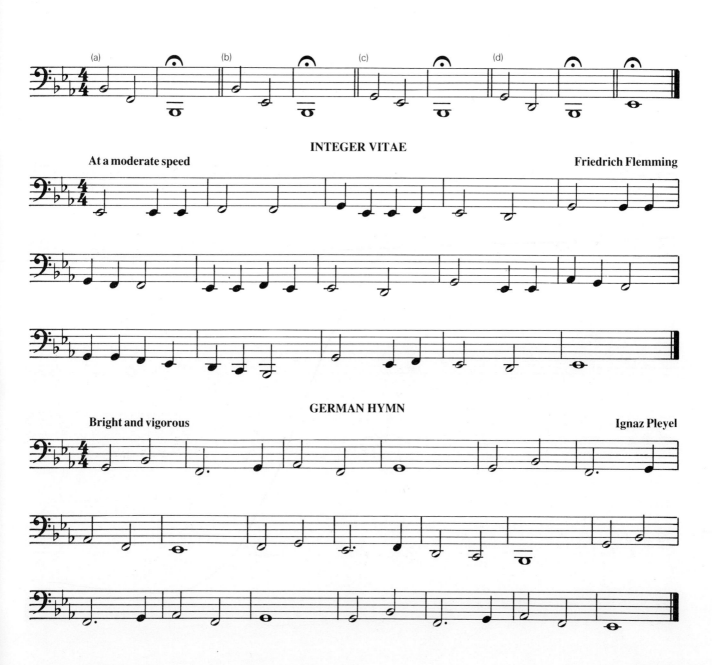

INTEGER VITAE

At a moderate speed

Friedrich Flemming

GERMAN HYMN

Bright and vigorous

Ignaz Pleyel

UNIT 4

Semibreve Rests

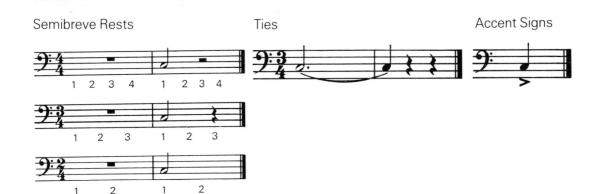

Ties

Accent Signs

A semibreve rest is used to show any complete bar of rest, regardless of the number of beats in the bar. When it occurs you must examine the time-signature to find the number of beats to be counted. Compare the three examples.

A tie is a curved line placed over or under two notes of the same pitch. The tie joins the notes together making one continuous note. In order to produce one continuous note the second note must not be tongued.

An accent sign placed over or under a note means that the note must be given a strong attack with the tongue. Often this strong attack is combined with a little 'punch' from the diaphragm.

Exercise 1

Exercise 2

Exercise 3

14

MARCH
"If all the world were paper"

In a bright march tempo

Derek Hyde

Musicianship

The ability to remember melodic phrases plays an important part in the development of musicianship. To help develop a melodic memory, try each week to memorise one of the shorter instrumental solos.

The grade 1 aural tests issued by the Associated Board of the Royal Schools of Music will help memory development and should be incorporated into the lesson at this stage.

MEXICAN MADNESS

Lively

Peter Wastall

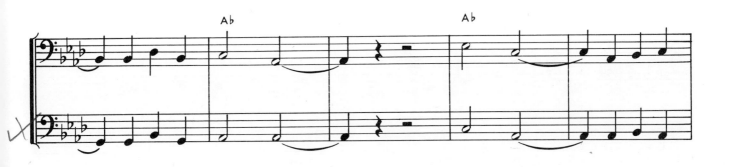

Semibreve Rests

Ties

Accent Signs

A semibreve rest is used to show any complete bar of rest, regardless of the number of beats in the bar. When it occurs you must examine the time-signature to find the number of beats to be counted. Compare the three examples.

A tie is a curved line placed over or under two notes of the same pitch. The tie joins the notes together making one continuous note. In order to produce one continuous note, the second note must not be tongued.

An accent sign placed over or under a note means that the note must be given a strong attack with the tongue. Often this strong attack is combined with a little 'punch' from the diaphragm.

Exercise 1

Exercise 2

Exercise 3

MARCH
"If all the world were paper"

In a bright march tempo

Adapted from a melody
by Derek Hyde

Musicianship

The ability to remember melodic phrases plays
an important part in the development of
musicianship. To help develop a melodic
memory, try each week to memorise one of the
shorter instrumental solos.

The grade 1 aural tests issued by the Associated
Board of the Royal Schools of Music will help
memory development and should be
incorporated into the lesson at this stage.

MEXICAN MADNESS

Peter Wastall

Lively

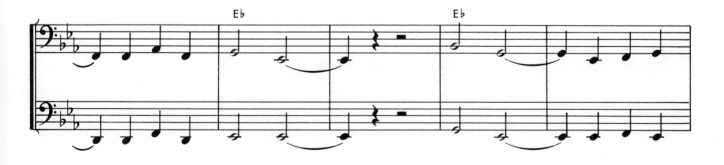

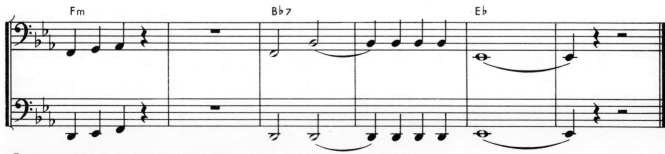

New Notes

D ⌐1

C

E♭   2   1   2

B♭ ⌐1 3

A New Key-signature

The two keys that use the key-signature with three flats are E♭ Major and C Minor. The music in this unit illustrates E♭ Major.

Repeat Signs

When a section has to be played twice, a pair of dots is placed at the beginning of the section and another at the end. Used in this way the dots act as buffers, bouncing you back to the previous set of dots. When there is only one set, the repeat is made back to the beginning of the piece.

E♭ Major

Exercise 1

Exercise 2

Exercise 3

BRANLE

Brightly

Nicholas Chédeville

Tone development

By now it should be possible to play middle B♭ with quite a 'rich' tone. The next exercise shows how to carry this rich tone downwards towards the low C. As you practise the exercise, carry out the following drill:

1. Listen closely to the sound, aiming for a full, even tone.
2. Check that the diaphragm is giving a firm support to the air stream.
3. As the notes descend, gradually enlarge the mouth cavity by slightly opening the gap between the teeth.

SERENADE

Fairly fast

Antonio Diabelli

A LITTLE PIECE

At a moderate speed

Robert Schumann

es   Repeat Signs

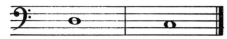   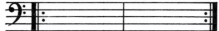

D   **C**

B♭   Open   1

When a section has to be played twice, a pair of
dots is placed at the beginning of the section and
another at the end. Used in this way the dots act
as buffers, bouncing you back to the previous set
of dots. When there is only one set, the repeat is
made back to the beginning of the piece.

Exercise 1

Exercise 2

Exercise 3

CHORALE

At a moderate speed

A 16th century German melody

Tone development

1. Use exercise (a) for comparing the embouchure formation for playing open notes F, B♭, D. Play the first three notes quite firmly, concentrating on accuracy of pitch.
2. In bar 2, breathe through the corners of the mouth keeping the mouthpiece still.
3. Commence bar 3 with an embouchure formation identical to that formed at the beginning of bar 1.
4. Repeat exercise (a) using the notes shown in exercise (b), (c) and (d).

"AH VOUS DIRAI-JE, MAMAN"

Fairly lively

A traditional French tune

A MELODY IN PHRYGIAN MODE
No. 28 from "Mikrokosmos" Vol. 1

Allegretto

Béla Bartók

Marks

Quavers

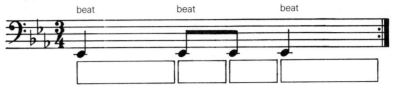

When a dot is placed over or under a note it indicates that the note is to sound detached. To achieve this, the note is played shorter than its printed value, often producing a clipped effect, rather like saying the word TAP.

The value of a quaver is half a crotchet: it is printed with a tail on the end of its stem. For ease of reading, groups of quavers usually have their tails joined together.

18/10/93   +   1/11/93

Exercise 1

Exercise 2

Exercise 3

BRANLE DE CHAMPAGNE

Fairly lively

Claude Gervaise

Aids to music reading

When you play quavers read them like a two syllable word. For example, when you read the word 'Doctor', you don't read 'Doc' then 'tor', you read 'Doctor'. This 'block' reading skill should be developed at the earliest possible stage of music reading. To help this development, each time quavers occur, make a conscious effort to read both notes at the same time.

CORUMBÁ

Lively (in the style of a bossa nova)

Peter Wastall

UNIT 7

New Notes

E♭	*	2
B♭	1	*

*Introduced in previous units.

Italian Terms

Italian terms describe how fast a piece is to be played and how loud or soft the music should sound. The terms which describe how loud or soft the music should sound are usually abbreviated. A table of the abbreviations is printed in Unit 11 where this aspect of technique is developed. A list of Italian terms is printed at the end of the book.

Slurs

A slur is a curved line placed over or under notes of different pitch. It indicates that the notes contained within the slur are to be played smoothly in one continuous breath. In order to do this, only the first note is tongued.

22/11/93 (Slurred exs).

Exercise 1

Exercise 2

Exercise 3

9/11/93

NUTFIELD

W. H. Monk

Moderato

Tone development

1. Produce the downward slur by a small relaxation of the embouchure muscles.
2. In bar 2, breathe through the corners of the mouth keeping the embouchure formation as still as possible.

3. Produce the upward slur by a small contraction of the embouchure muscles.
4. Repeat exercise (a) using the notes shown in exercise (b) (c) and (d).

Note: Play either the Eb exercise or the BBb exercise as appropriate. DO NOT PLAY THE PARTS TOGETHER.

LAND OF OUR FATHERS

A traditional Welsh tune

UNIT 8

A New Note

Eb   2

Bb   2

Keys and Key-signatures

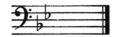

In flat keys, the name of the major key can be found by counting four letter names down from the last flat. The key-signature of exercise 1 has Bb and Eb, therefore the name of the major key is Bb Major.

31/1/94

Exercise 1

mf

Exercise 2

mf

f

Scales and arpeggios

Eb major, to be played from memory

7/2/94

GERMAN DANCE

Moderato

L. van Be...

Musicianship

Articulation (tonguing and slurring used in wind music) plays an important part in the creation of expression. It is the speech of music and can be thought of as the music equivalent of elocution. The tongue must produce a definite and clear attack, aided by well-prepared breath support.

In this unit concentrate on improving your articulation, using it to give additional meaning to the phrases.

DUO
Adapted from "St. Petersburg"

Andante

Dmitry Bortniansky

27

ERT PIECES FOR UNITS 1-8

...ments to the concert pieces
...separate accompaniment
...uld be used to provide
experience in playing with an accompanist.
'Andante' by Gurlitt is an example of music
that has been set for early grade
examinations.

TUBA-TALK

DEREK HYDE

ROMANCE
"Homage to Peter Ilyich"

Molto moderato

KEITH RAMON COLE

Grde I

ANDANTE
from "First Steps" op.82

CORNELIUS GURLITT
(1820 – 1901)
arr. PETER WASTALL

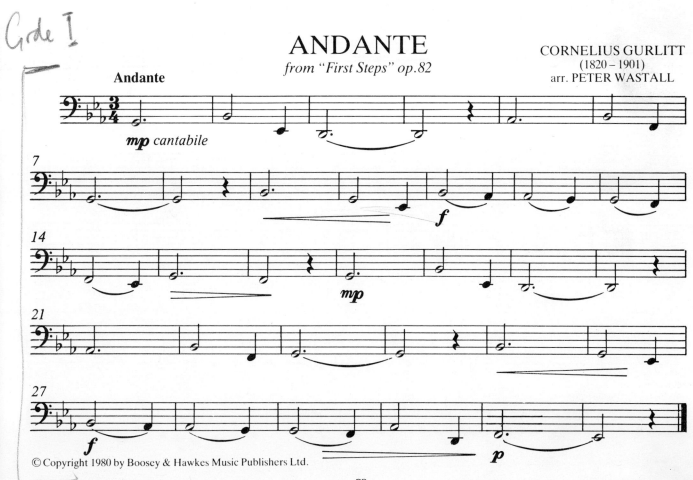

29

UNIT 9

A New Note

♭𝆗

E♭ 1/3 or 4

B♭ *

*Introduced in unit 5 for B♭ Tuba.

Dotted Crotchets

beat   beat   beat

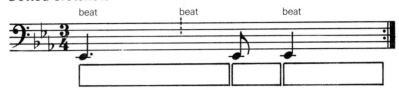

Since a dot after a note lengthens that note by
half its value, the value of a dotted crotchet will
be one and a half crotchet beats; the same
length of sound as three quavers added together.
Look at the example, then study the similarity of
bars 2 and 3 in the second exercise.

Exercise 1

Exercise 2

Exercise 3

THE EMPEROR OF GERMANY'S MARCH

Jeremiah Clarke

Tone development

1. Use this set of exercises to develop maximum vibration at the lip centre.
2. Check that the facial muscles are properly formed at all times, particularly the corners of the mouth outside the mouthpiece.
3. As you descend, gradually enlarge the mouth cavity by slightly opening the gap between the teeth.
4. Use 4th valve for low B♭ on non-compensating tubas.

FANFARE

Nicholas Chédeville

31

then go to p 40.

UNIT 10

New Notes

Accidentals

*Because of the accidental, both these notes are
D♭.

When a flat (or sharp) is used that is not in the
key-signature it is called an accidental.
An accidental lasts until the next bar-line and
because of this, affects any subsequent note of
the same pitch in that bar.

	D♭	D♭
E♭	1	*
B♭	2 3	2

*Introduced in unit 3 for E♭ Tuba.

Exercise 1

Exercise 2

Exercise 3

Scales and arpeggios

Bb Major, to be played from memory.

Tone development

1. Use the first note to establish a good embouchure formation.
2. In bars 2 and 3, ensure maximum flexibility by using a minimum amount of mouthpiece pressure against the lips.

3. Pay strict attention to the slurs, even if a note fails to 'speak', resist the temptation to tongue it.
4. Repeat exercise (a) using the notes shown in exercises (b) (c) and (d).

LE PETIT-RIEN

François Couperin ("Le Grand")

ELLACOMBE

German traditional tune

UNIT 11

Natural Signs

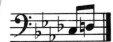

A natural sign is used to cancel a flat or sharp. Since it is a type of accidental, it will only last for the bar in which it is printed. However, if a note that has been altered occurs again in the next bar, an additional accidental is often used to confirm that the note has returned to its original pitch.

31/10/94

Italian terms

pp   very soft   ***ff***   very loud

p   soft   ***f***   loud

mp   moderately soft   ***mf***   moderately loud

gradually softer   gradually louder

Italian terms also describe the mood of a piece, changes of speed and large repeats such as da capo. As with Italian terms introduced earlier, English translations can be found at the end of the book.

A table of Italian terms which show how loud or soft the music should sound is printed above. It should be used in conjunction with the tuning technique introduced in this unit.

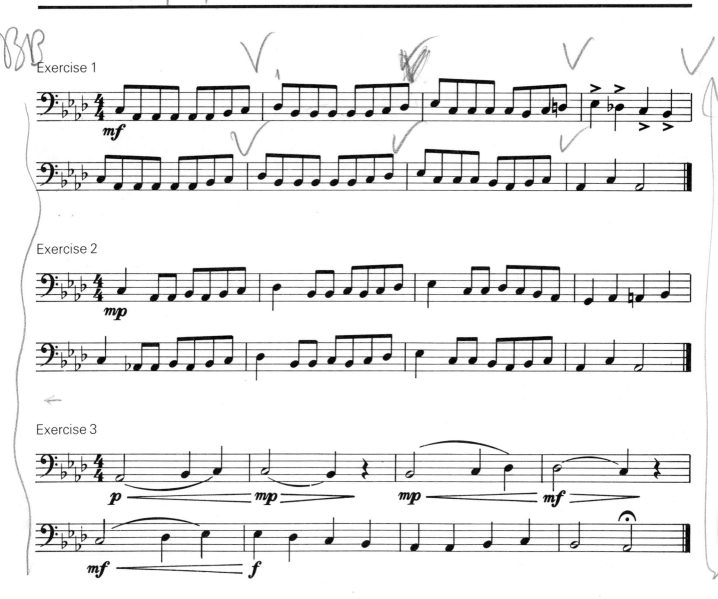

Exercise 1

Exercise 2

Exercise 3

A LITTLE PIECE

Cornelius Gurlitt

Musicianship

Crescendos and diminuendos play an important part in creating expression but need careful use since they also have an effect on tuning. Basically, a crescendo (produced by increasing the air pressure) will make a note go sharp, and a diminuendo (produced by reducing the air pressure) will make a note go flat.

To stabilise the tuning, allow the lip aperture to open slightly during a crescendo, and close slightly during a diminuendo.

DUETTO

J. B. de Boismortier

UNIT 12

New Notes

E

Eb   2 or 1
      4   2
           3
           ↓

Bb   2

↓ Lip down on instruments without compensating tubing.

Quaver Rests

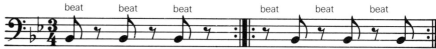

A quaver rest is a rest for half a crotchet beat. Bar 1 of the example shows it occurring on the second half of a crotchet beat, and bar 2 on the first half. The rhythmic difference between the two rhythms should be clearly understood before playing their related exercises.

Minor Keys

To find the name of a minor key, count three letter names down inclusive from the name of the major key. To find out whether the music is in a major or a minor key, compare it with the appropriate scale.

F Minor

Exercise 1

Exercise 2

Exercise 3

COVENTRY CAROL

An English 16th century carol

Fourth valve technique – E♭ Tuba

1. On a non-compensating 4-valved E♭ tuba, use valves 2 and 4 for low E. Practise this fingering in exercises (a) (c) and (d). Apply the fingering throughout this unit.

2. On a 3-valved E♭ tuba use valves 1, 2 and 3 for low E, but be aware that the tuning is likely to be very sharp. Practise exercises (a) (c) and (d) very slowly, concentrating on lipping the low E in tune.

3. On a compensating E♭ tuba, either of the fingerings shown for low E may be used. However, in many passages valves 2 and 4 are often the most convenient. Practise exercises (b) (c) and (d) with 4th valve low F, and 2 and 4 low E, to develop skill at using these fingerings.

ETUDE

Antonio Diabelli

37

UNIT 13

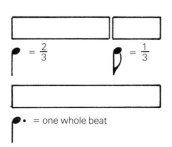

Compound Time

= one whole beat

Compound Time-signatures

When the natural pulse of a piece divides itself into thirds of a beat, the music is said to be in compound time. The various notes retain the same value in relation to each other; for instance, there are still two quavers in a crotchet, but their value in relation to the beat is changed to the values shown in the example.

To show the new note values a new set of time-signatures is used. The example shows six-eight, indicating two dotted crotchet beats in a bar. A chart showing the complete range of compound time-signatures and how they are applied is printed at the end of the book.

Exercise 1

Exercise 2

Exercise 3

MARMOTTE

Allegretto

L. van

Aids to music reading

When reading notes which are thirds of a beat, read them as if they were three-syllable words. As an example of this, try the first exercise thinking the word TENTATIVE as you play each group. When playing the pieces, apply this reading principle to all rhythmic groups contained within one beat.

DUO

Leggiero

François Garnier

Teacher

Pupil

Sharp Signs

B **F♯**

E♭	2 / 3	2 / 3
B♭	1 / 2	2 / 3

The sign for raising a note by half a tone is called a sharp sign. Like the flat sign it can be placed immediately before the note it affects, or it can be placed at the beginning of each staff to form a key-signature.

A New Key-signature

*Because of the key-signature both these notes must be played as F♯.

In sharp keys, the name of the major key can be found by counting one letter name up from the last sharp. The example shows a key-signature with F♯, therefore the name of the major key is G Major.

31/10/94.

Exercise 1

Exercise 2

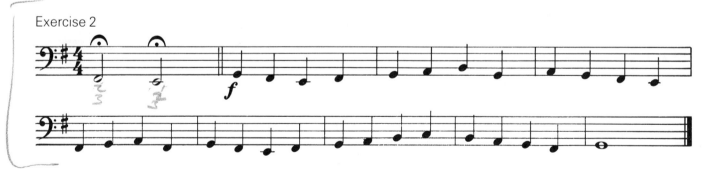

Exercise 3

Scales and arpeggios 31/10/94.

C Major, to be played from memory

Tone development

1. During each exercise, maintain a flexible embouchure, but keep the air pressure strong and even.
2. Strive to keep the tone quality uniform, taking particular care with the lower notes.
3. Pay strict attention to the slurs, even if a note fails to "speak", resist the temptation to tongue it.
4. Repeat exercise (a) using the notes shown in exercises (b) (c) and (d).

A LITTLE PIECE

Antonio Diabelli

LULLABY

Franz Schubert

41

UNIT 15

Tenuto Signs

1st and 2nd time bars

A tenuto sign placed over or under a note means that the note is to be played with a lingering pressure. Usually it is also associated with a type of tonguing where one syllable is added to another without any noticeable break in the air stream.

Sometimes the ending of a repeated section is altered the second time through. When this occurs, 1st and 2nd time bars are used. The example is taken from "Ein' feste Burg" in which

bars 1 – 4 are played quite normally the first time through, but when they are repeated the first time bar is omitted and the second time bar played instead.

Exercise 1

Exercise 2

Exercise 3

EIN' FESTE BURG

A chorale by M. Luther
adapted by J. S. Bach

Musicianship

Sometimes the general character of a piece suggests that many of the notes should be played staccato. When this occurs, the dots on top of the notes are often omitted, leaving it to the instrumentalist to interpret the music in a staccato style. The "Duo" by Chédeville is an example of this.

DUO IN G MINOR

Esprit Chédeville

CONCERT PIECES FOR UNITS 9-15

As with earlier concert pieces, piano accompaniments should be used to provide experience in playing with an accompanist. 'Air' by Gretry and 'Make Mine a Tuba' by Norton are examples of music that has been set for early grade examinations.

PROMENADE

Jaunty and fairly fast

DEREK HYDE

© Copyright 1980 by Boosey & Hawkes Music Publishers Ltd.

Grde II A

AIR
from "Richard Coeur de Lion"

ANDRE GRETRY
(1741 – 1813)
arr. PETER WASTALL

Moderato

© Copyright 1980 by Boosey & Hawkes Music Publishers Ltd.

MAKE MINE A TUBA

CHRISTOPHER NORTON

Moderato

UNIT 16

Semiquavers

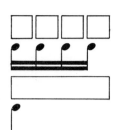

Syncopation

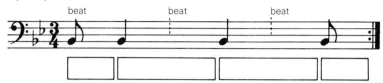

The value of a semiquaver is a quarter of a crotchet; it is printed with two tails on the end of its stem. As with quavers, all the tails contained in one beat can be joined together.

A new rhythm, called syncopation, is produced when strongly accented notes occur between the beats instead of coinciding with them.

As shown in the duet, the surrounding quavers are usually played staccato to help bounce the syncopated notes off the beat.

Exercise 1

Exercise 2

Scales and arpeggios

C Minor (harmonic form), to be played from memory

LARGHETTO

Larghetto

W. A. Mozart

Aids to music reading

With blocks of four semiquavers, read each group as you would a four-syllable word. Start with passages that are easy to play (such as the two exercises shown opposite) and make a conscious effort to read each block of four semiquavers as a single unit.

A SYNCOPATED DUET

Allegretto

François Garnier

UNIT 17

New Notes

Dotted Quavers

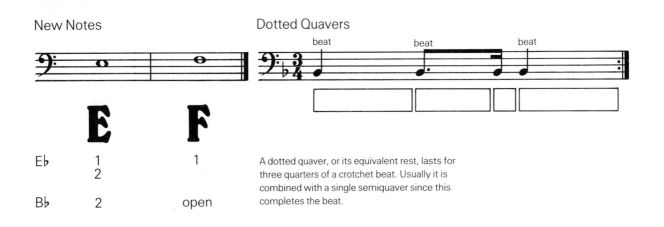

	E	F
E♭	1 2	1
B♭	2	open

A dotted quaver, or its equivalent rest, lasts for three quarters of a crotchet beat. Usually it is combined with a single semiquaver since this completes the beat.

STUDY No.1

Hipployte Niessel

Adagio

48

St. ANTHONY CHORALE

Joseph Haydn

Aids to music reading

The reading technique for a single semiquaver is to group the semiquaver with the note which follows. In lively movements, a useful way to achieve this is to pronounce the two notes as if saying the word TODAY. As an example, play the first note of the "Soldier's March" by Schumann, then think TODAY as you play the next two notes. This reading technique can be used every time a dotted rhythm occurs.

SOLDIER'S MARCH

R. Schumann

UNIT 18

Semiquaver Rests

Note patterns using Semiquavers

A semiquaver rest is a rest for a quarter of a crotchet beat. Notice that it is similar to the semiquaver note, being printed with two tails. Examples of the semiquaver rest can be found in the duet.

By combining semiquavers with quavers, several new rhythm patterns can be formed. The examples should be studied carefully before playing the exercises.

Exercise 1

Exercise 2

Scales and arpeggios

F Major, to be played from memory

SHORE'S TRUMPET TUNE

Pomposo

From an eighteenth century
collection of trumpet tunes

Musicianship

As you play the "Duetto" by Devienne, notice that the general character is one of smoothness. To achieve this smoothness, use a very gentle type of tonguing, rather like pronouncing the syllable DAH. When playing in this manner, we say we are interpreting the music in a legato style. Compare the style with that needed for playing "Shore's trumpet tune", where the mood demands that a vigorous, accented type of tonguing be used.

DUETTO IN G MINOR

Andante

Adapted from a duet
by F. Devienne

UNIT 19

New Notes

F♯   G

Eb   2   Open

Bb   *   *

Double Names for Notes

C♯ = Db   D♯ = Eb   F♯ = Gb   A♯ = Bb   G♯ = Ab

The interval between A and B is one whole tone. Since a sharp raises a note by half a tone, and a flat lowers a note by half a tone, it follows that A♯ and Bb are different names for the same note. Double names can be given to all the flats and sharps learned so far.

*Bb Tuba plays lower notes where indicated.

STUDY No.2

Hippolyte Niessel

Scales and arpeggios

D Minor (harmonic form) to be played from memory

Tone development

1. Concentrate on a muscular contraction of the embouchure for playing these smaller interval lip-slurs.
2. Use bars 1 and 2 to establish the muscular feel of the exercise.

3. Play bar 3 at a speed comfortable to your embouchure development. Be careful to maintain the rhythm since upward slurs are often slow to respond on the tuba.

4. Repeat exercise (a) using the notes shown in exercises (b) (c) (d) and (e).

WALTZ

Andante

Franz Schubert

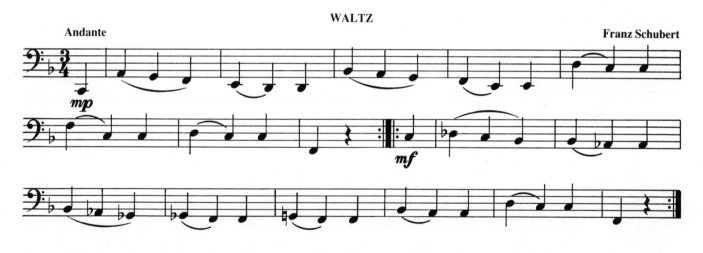

CONTREDANSE

Allegretto

Joseph Haydn

D. C. al Fine

20

Three-two Time

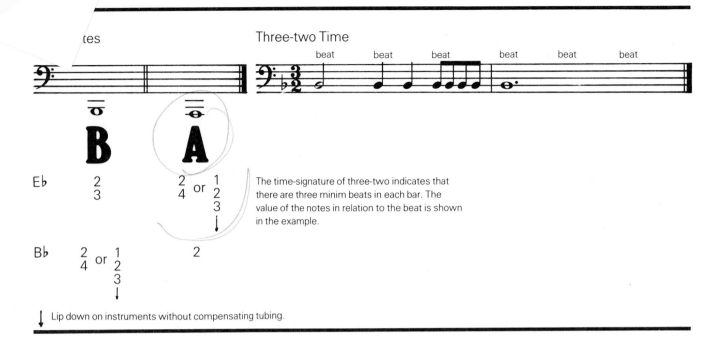

tes

| | beat | beat | beat | beat | beat | beat |

Eb
2
3

2 or 1
4 2
3
↓

Bb
2 or 1
4 2
3
↓

2

The time-signature of three-two indicates that there are three minim beats in each bar. The value of the notes in relation to the beat is shown in the example.

↓ Lip down on instruments without compensating tubing.

Exercise

J. Weissenborn

Scales and arpeggios

F Minor (harmonic form) to be played from memory.

D Major, to be played from memory

Bb major, to be played from memory

GAGLIARDA

Moderato

Girolamo Frescobaldo

mf *dolce* *rit.* *cresc.* *f*

Fourth valve technique – B♭ Tuba

1. On a non-compensating 4-valved B♭ tuba, use valves 2 and 4 for low B. Practise this fingering in exercises (b) (c) and (d). Apply the fingering throughout this unit.

2. On a 3-valved B♭ tuba use valves 1, 2 and 3 for low B but be aware that the tuning is likely to be very sharp. Practise exercises (b) (c) and (d) very slowly, concentrating on lipping the low B in tune.

3. On a compensating B♭ tuba, either of the fingerings shown for low B may be used. However, in many passages valves 2 and 4 are often the most convenient. Practise exercises (a) (b) and (c) with 4th valve low C, and 2 and 4 low B, to develop skill at using these fingerings.

(a)   (b)   (c)   (d)

DUO

Moderato

Hippolyte Niessel

f *f* *mp* *mp* *f* *f*

21

Change of Time signature

	Ab	Ab	G
Eb	1	*	*
Bb	*	1	1 2

Sometimes a time-signature is changed during the course of a piece. When this occurs the speed of the beat usually remains the same; it is the pulse pattern that changes. The example is taken from the "Cantilena" by Arpád Balázs.

*As in unit 19, Eb Tuba plays upper notes and Bb Tuba lower notes.

STUDY No.3

Andantino

Hippolyte Niessel

CANTILENA

Molto legato

Árpád Balázs
(b. 1937)

Tone development

1. Descend by relaxation, making sure the facial muscles remain under control.
2. If the lower notes fail to respond, check that the mouth cavity is sufficiently open and that the lips are able to vibrate freely.

3. If a note fails to 'speak' in the ascending slur, check that the diaphragm is giving a firm support to the air stream and that the air pressure is strong and even.

4. Repeat exercise (a) using the notes shown in exercises (b) (c) and (d).

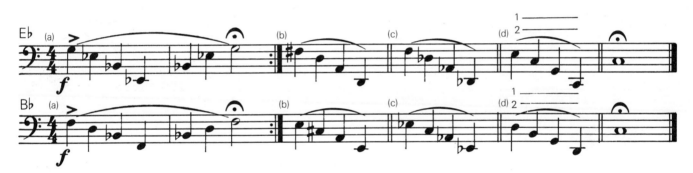

THIRD MODE MELODY

Largo

Thomas Tallis

UNIT 22

Triplets

Rests of Several Bars

1	2	3 (1st bar)
2	2	3 (2nd bar)
3	2	3 (3rd bar)

etc.

A tripet can be defined as 'three notes played in the time of two notes of the same value' (for instance, three quavers played in the time of two quavers). The number 3 is placed over or under them to show the momentary change of note value.

When a rest of several bars is required, only one bar is used, a black line is usually drawn in this bar, and the number of complete bars to be counted placed on top. The example is taken from the concert piece on p.60.

Exercise 1

Wilhelm Popp

Scales and arpeggios

G Major, to be played from memory

Ab Major, to be played from memory

G Minor (harmonic form) to be played from memory

ARIA

Andante larghetto

G. F. Handel

Musicianship

Both pieces in this unit have performing directions relating to their mood: the Handel "Aria" is marked dolce espressivo, and the "Duo" by Niessel grazioso. As you practise, try to create these moods, and in particular use the shapes of the phrases for displaying control over the dynamics. In the "Aria", the repeated notes create good opportunities for expressive tenuto playing. The important thing to remember is that performing directions are a starting point for creating your own expression.

DUO No.2

Grazioso

Hippolyte Niessel

CONCERT PIECES FOR UNITS 16-22

'The Merry Peasant' by Schumann, 'Quick Dance' by Bogár and 'Jimbo's Lullaby' by Debussy are examples of music that has been set for early grade examinations.

SOLSTICE

KEITH RAMON COLE

ARIA
"O Isis and Osiris"

W. A. MOZART
(1756 – 1791)
arr. PETER WASTALL

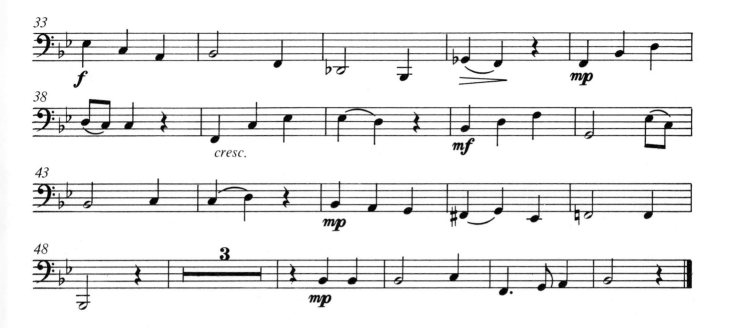

JIMBO'S LULLABY
from "Children's Corner"

CLAUDE DEBUSSY
(1862 – 1918)
arr. PETER WASTALL

At a fairly moderate speed

THE MERRY PEASANT
from "Album for the Young"

ROBERT SCHUMANN
(1810 – 1856)
arr. PETER WASTALL

Cheerful and lively

QUICK DANCE

ISTVÁN BOGÁR
(b. 1937)

Vivace

Printed by
Halstan & Co. Ltd., Amersham, Bucks., England

BASIC FINGERING CHART E♭TUBA

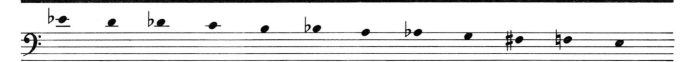

E♭	D	D♭	C	B	B♭	A	A♭	G	F#	F	E
Open	2	1	1 2	2 3	Open	2	1	Open	2	1	1 2

E♭	D	D♭	C	B	B♭	A	A♭	G	F#	F	E
Open	2	1	1 2	2 3	Open	2	1	1 2	2 3	1 or 4 3	1 2 2 or 4 3 ↓

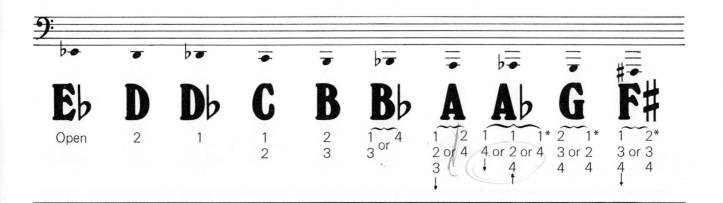

E♭	D	D♭	C	B	B♭	A	A♭	G	F#
Open	2	1	1 2	2 3	1 or 4 3	1 2 or 4 2 or 4 3 ↓	1 1 4 or 2 or 4 4	1* 2 1* 3 or 2 4 4	1 2* 3 or 3 4 4 ↓

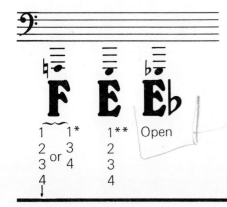

F	E	E♭
1 1* 2 or 3 3 4 4 ↓	1** 2 3 4	Open

↓   Lip down on instruments without compensating tubing.

↑   Lip up on instruments without compensating tubing.

*   Best fingering for instruments with compensating tubing.

**   Not available on instruments without compensating tubing.

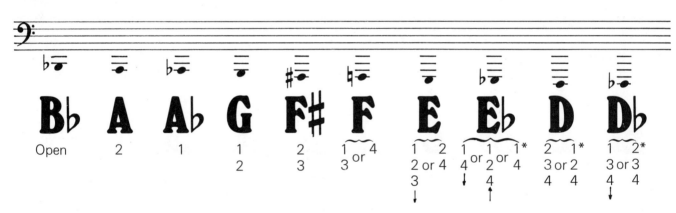

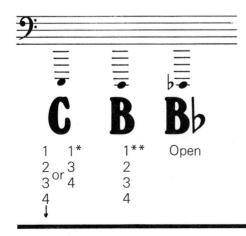

| Lip down on instruments without compensating tubing. |
| Lip up on instruments without compensating tubing. |
| * Best fingering for instruments with compensating tubing. |
| ** Not available on instruments without compensating tubing. |

Left hand position

Notice how the left hand supports the trumpet, enabling the right hand fingertips to be positioned over the valves

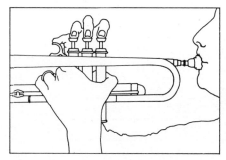

Right hand position

Notice how the right hand thumb provides a firm base from which the fingers can depress the valves

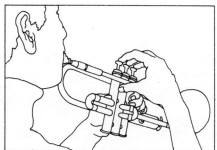

Mouthpiece placement

In most cases, the mouthpiece should be placed centrally on the lips, with equal proportions of top and bottom lip showing inside the mouthpiece when a visualiser is used

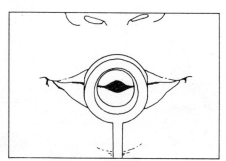

Embouchure formation

1. Mouthpiece held lightly against the lips with just enough pressure to stop air from escaping.
2. Cheek muscles firm (ie. the cheeks must never be allowed to balloon outwards).
3. Jaw positioned so that both lips can vibrate freely.

Open notes

In keeping with other brass instruments, the trumpet, cornet and flugel horn have a range of notes that can be produced without depressing any of the valves. After producing the initial 'buzz', try to produce one of the open notes, starting on whichever is most comfortable to play.

Points to note:

1. Usually the first sounds are either C, G or low C. The main objective will be to play G.

2. If the first open notes are higher than G, relax the centre of the aperture. If the first open notes are lower than G, firm the muscles at the lip centre.

3. Once the G is established, relax down to the low C and compare the embouchure formation required to play these two basic sounds.

After experimenting with the open notes, compare the sounds of G, F, E, D and C.

Try to start each note with a tongue movement similar to that used when pronouncing the letter 'T'.

Trumpet and cornet pitch

The trumpet and cornet are transposing instruments, their notes sounding a major second lower than the printed notes. Pupils using a piano to check pitch should play G on the trumpet or cornet to sound the same as F on the piano.

G	F	E	D	C
Open	1	1 2	1 3	Open

PREPARATORY MATERIAL FOR UNIT 1

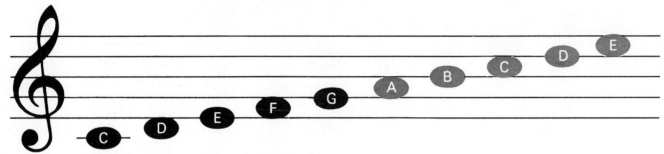

These are the notes shown in the fingering chart.

Notation

Printed notes are also named after the first seven letters of the alphabet. From the example it can be seen that they are placed on a staff (the name of the five lines), each line and each space counting as one letter name.

The Treble Clef

Since the same seven letter names are used for all instruments (i.e. those that produce low notes, as well as those that produce high notes) a clef sign is placed at the beginning of each staff to establish exact pitch. Music for the trumpet, cornet and flugel horn uses the treble clef.

Note Lengths

The length of time a note is played is measured by the beat; the difference in length being shown by various types of note. The three types used in unit 1 are:

crotchet   minim   semibreve

Play the following crotchets trying to hold each for exactly the same amount of time.

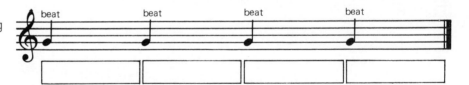

Now play the following minims, holding each note for the whole of beats one and two added together.

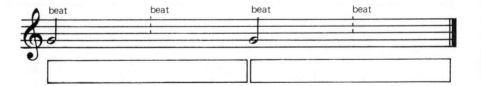

Now play a semibreve, trying to hold the note for exactly four beats.

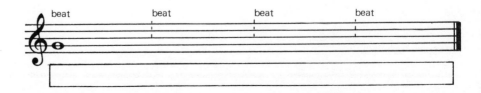

Bars and bar lines

Bar line   Bar line

Beats usually group themselves into regular patterns of either two, three or four; to show these patterns, the music is divided by bar lines into bars.

A double bar-line is used to separate differing sections of music within a single piece.

A thin/thick double bar indicates the end of a piece or exercise.

Time Signatures

A time-signature is placed at the beginning of each piece of music to show how many beats there are in a bar, and the type of note that equals one beat. It is printed in fractional form, the value of the crotchet being shown as a fraction of a semibreve.

2/4 showing 2 crotchet beats in each bar

3/4 showing 3 crotchet beats in each bar

4/4 showing 4 crotchet beats in each bar

UNIT 1

Tuning and pitch

written   sounds

The trumpet, cornet and flugel horn are transposing instruments, their notes sounding a major second lower than the printed notes. Pupils using a piano to check pitch should play G to sound the same as F on the piano.

E G B D F
F A C E

Notes and Fingerings
(summarised from P. 2 - 5)

G   **F**   **E**   **D**   **C**

Open   1   1   1   Open
        2   3

F A C E

Exercise 1

G   F   F   G   G   F   F   G   G

Exercise 2

F   E   E   F   F   E   E   F   F

Exercise 3

E   C   C   E   E   E   D   D   E

C   D   E   F   G   F   E   D   C

Exercise 4

G   G   F   F   G   G   E   E   F   F   E   D   D

G   G   F   F   G   G   E   E   F   F   E   C   C

Exercise 5

Musicianship

When you practise the instrumental solos, notice how the notes form patterns almost as if they were words in a rhyme. In music these note patterns are called phrases; to help identify them, phrases in some early pieces have been marked with brackets. Breaths are normally taken at the ends of phrases; additional breaths can be taken, but these must be discreet so as not to disturb the natural flow of the phrase.

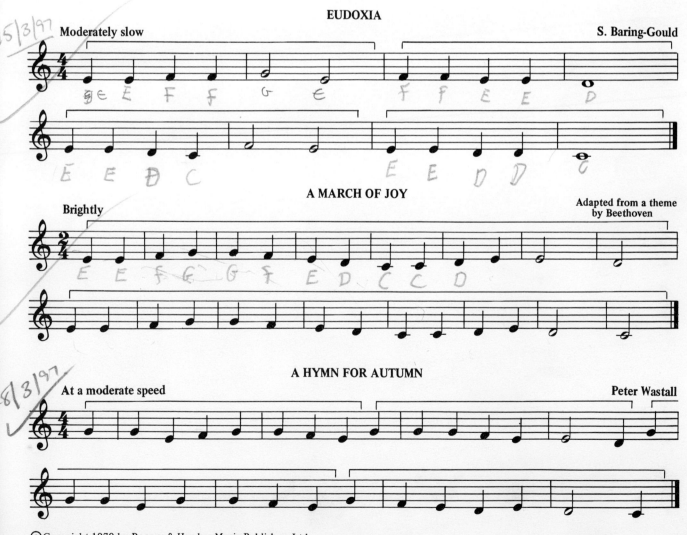

EUDOXIA

Moderately slow

S. Baring-Gould

A MARCH OF JOY

Brightly

Adapted from a theme by Beethoven

A HYMN FOR AUTUMN

At a moderate speed

Peter Wastall

UNIT 2

The Pause sign

Rests

When a pause sign is placed over a note, the beat stops and the note is played for a period of time longer than its printed value. During the first section of this book the pause will be used mainly in the exercises, identifying individual notes that are to be sustained for as long as possible.

The length of time in which notes are not played is shown by various rests, each note having an equivalent rest. The example shows the minim rest (two beats of silence) and the crotchet rest (one beat of silence).

3/4/97.

FFIGYSBREN

At a moderate speed

A traditional Welsh tune

Tone development

One of the best ways to develop a full tone is to play individual long notes. In the exercise that follows, listen closely to the sound and check these vital points.

1. Diaphragm giving a light support to the air stream.
2. Trumpet held in such a position that both lips can vibrate freely.
3. Facial muscles firm, but not gripping.

LET'S BEGUINE
(A duet for pupil and teacher)

In the style of a beguine

Peter Wastall

*Concert pitch chord symbols for keyboard accompaniment.

9

P.T.O

UNIT 3

New Notes

Dotted Minims

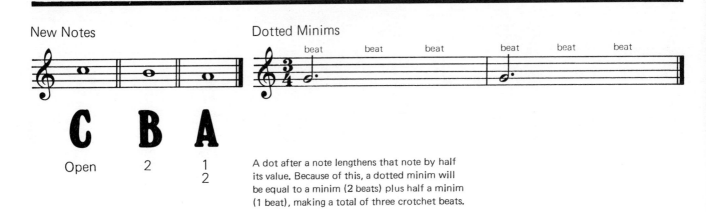

C   **B**   **A**

Open   2   1
               2

A dot after a note lengthens that note by half
its value. Because of this, a dotted minim will
be equal to a minim (2 beats) plus half a minim
(1 beat), making a total of three crotchet beats.

Exercise 1

Exercise 2

Exercise 3

10

Musicianship

The ability to remember melodic phrases plays an important part in the development of musicianship. To help develop a melodic memory, try each week to memorise one of the shorter instrumental solos.

The grade 1 aural tests issued by the Associated Board of the Royal Schools of Music will help memory development and should be incorporated into the lesson at this stage.

SWIM, SWAN, SWIM!

Lively

Derek Hyde

© Copyright 1973 by Boosey & Hawkes Music Publishers Ltd.

CHORALE MELODY

At a moderate speed

German, 16th century

"AH VOUS DIRAI-JE, MAMAN"

Allegretto 10/4/97.

A traditional French tune

Go to page 13.

UNIT 4

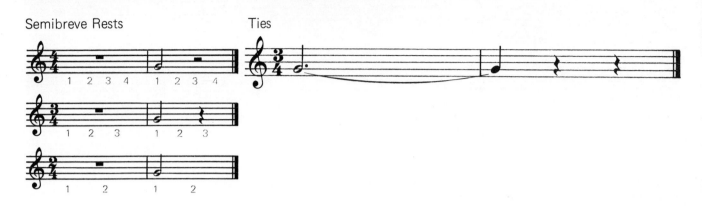

Semibreve Rests

Ties

A semibreve rest is used to show any complete bar of rest, regardless of the number of beats in the bar. When it occurs you must examine the time-signature to find the number of beats to be counted. Compare the three examples.

A tie is a curved line placed over or under two notes of the same pitch. The tie joins the notes together making one continuous note. In order to produce one continuous note the second note must not be tongued.

Exercise 1

Exercise 2

Exercise 3

MARCH
"If all the world were paper"

In a bright march tempo

Derek Hyde

Tone development

1. Use exercise (a) for comparing the embouchure formation for playing open notes C-G-C.
2. Play the first note with a relatively strong air pressure, keeping the diaphragm moderately firm.

3. During the exercise, progressively lower the diaphragm and tongue levels by using the syllables 'TOO-TA-TAAH'.
4. Encourage the lips to vibrate freely, but keep the corners of the mouth in their correct position at all times.
5. Repeat the drill for each exercise.

MEXICAN MADNESS

Peter Wastall

UNIT 5

A New Note

1

Flat Signs

Every note used in music can be raised or lowered half a tone. The sign for lowering a note half a tone is the flat sign shown in the example. Compare the sound of B♭ with the natural B used in units 3 and 4.

Slurs

A slur is a curved line placed over or under notes of a different pitch. It indicates that the notes contained within the slur are to be played smoothly in one continuous breath. In order to do this only the first note is tongued.

Exercise 1

Exercise 2

Exercise 3

14

Exercise 4

Tone development

1. Produce the upward slur by a small contraction of the embouchure muscles; at the same time slightly raise the tongue and diaphragm levels.

2. In bar 2, breathe through the corners of the mouth keeping the embouchure formation as still as possible.

3. Produce the downward slur by a small relaxation of the embouchure muscles and a slight lowering of the tongue and diaphragm levels.

4. Repeat exercise (a) using the notes shown in exercises (b) (c) and (d). Use valves 1 & 3 for both notes in exercise (d).

MINUETTO

Fairly lively

Adapted from a Minuet by James Hook

ARIA

At a moderate speed

Friedrich Gluck

15

UNIT 6

Keys and Key-signatures

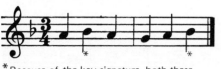

* Because of the key-signature, both these notes must be played as B♭.

When flat signs are placed at the beginning of each staff they are called a key-signature. Each flat is placed on a specific line or space indicating that every note with that letter name is to be played as if the flat were against the note. The two keys that use the key-signature with one flat are: F Major and D Minor. The music in this unit is in F Major.

Quavers

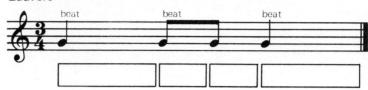

The value of a quaver is half a crotchet; it is printed with a tail on the end of its stem. For ease of reading, groups of quavers usually have their tails joined together.

F Major

Exercise 1

Exercise 2

Exercise 3

BRANLE DE CHAMPAGNE

Fairly fast

Claude Gervaise

Aids to music reading

When you play quavers, read them like a two-syllable word. For example, when you read the word 'Doctor', you don't read 'Doc' then 'tor', you read 'Doctor'. This "block" reading skill should be developed at the earliest possible stage of music reading. To help this development, each time quavers occur, make a conscious effort to read both notes at the same time.

CORUMBÁ

Lively (in the style of a bossa-nova)

Peter Wastall

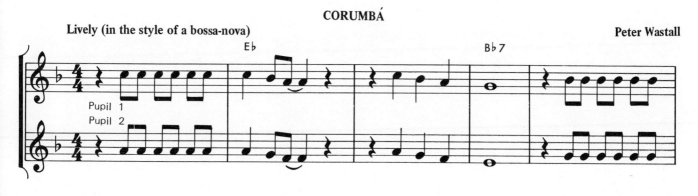

Pupil 1
Pupil 2

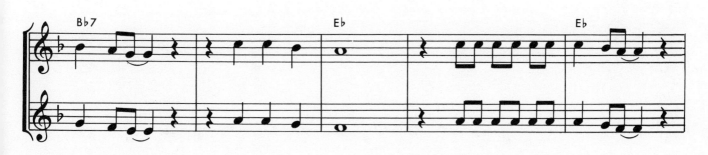

17

UNIT 7

New Notes

Keys and Key-signatures

B 2 **A** 1 2

The two keys that have no flats (or sharps) in their key-signature are: C Major and A Minor. The music in this unit illustrates C Major.

C Major

Exercise 1

Exercise 2

Exercise 3

18

SERENADE

Antonio Diabelli

Fairly fast

Tone development

1. Use this set of exercises to develop maximum vibration at the lip centre.
2. Check that the facial muscles are properly formed at all times, particularly the corners of the mouth outside the mouthpiece.
3. As you descend, enlarge the mouth cavity by slightly opening the gap between the teeth.
4. Check the angle you are holding the trumpet to ensure that the bottom lip is free to vibrate.

LAND OF OUR FATHERS

At a moderate speed

A traditional Welsh tune

19

UNIT 8

Staccato Marks

When a dot is placed over or under a note it indicates that the note is to sound detached. To achieve this, the note is played shorter than its printed value, often producing a clipped effect, rather like saying the word TAP.

Repeat Signs

When a section has to be played twice, a pair of dots is placed at the beginning of the section and another at the end. Used in this way, the dots act as buffers, bouncing you back to the previous set of dots. When there is only one set, the repeat is made back to the beginning of the piece.

Italian Terms

Italian terms describe how fast a piece is to be played and how loud or soft the music should sound. The terms which describe how loud or soft the music should sound are usually abbreviated. A table of the abbreviations is printed in Unit 12 where this aspect of technique is developed.
A list of Italian terms is printed at the end of the book.

Exercise 1

Exercise 2

Exercise 3

GERMAN DANCE

Moderato

L. van Beethoven

Tone development

1. Use the first note to establish a good embouchure formation.
2. In bars 2 and 3, check that the tongue and diaphragm levels move slightly up when the notes ascend, and move slightly down when the notes descend.
3. Pay strict attention to the slurs; even if a note fails to "speak", resist the temptation to tongue it.
4. Repeat exercise (a) using the notes shown in exercises (b) (c) and (d).

(a)   (b)   (c)   (d)

DUO
Adapted from "St. Petersburg"

Andante

Dmitry Bortniansky

CONCERT PIECES FOR UNITS 1-8

Piano accompaniments to the concert pieces are available in a separate accompaniment book. These should be used to provide experience in playing with an accompanist. 'Minuetto' by Hook is an example of music that has been set for early grade examinations.

MINUETTO
from Sonata No. 3, op. 99

JAMES HOOK
(1746-1827)
arr. PETER WASTALL

© Copyright 1975 by Boosey & Hawkes Music Publishers Ltd.

CHORUS
from "Paris and Helen"

C. W. GLUCK
(1714-1787)
arr. PETER WASTALL

© Copyright 1979 by Boosey & Hawkes Music Publishers Ltd.

22

GRANITE

With a solid rock beat

KEITH RAMON COLE

UNIT 9

New Notes

D
1

F#
2

Sharp Signs

The sign for raising a note by half a tone is called a sharp. Like the flat sign, it can be placed immediately before the note it affects, or it can be placed at the beginning of each staff to form a key-signature.

A New Key-signature

*Because of the key-signature, both these notes must be played as F♯.

The two keys that use the key-signature with one sharp are: G Major and E Minor. The exercises and pieces in this unit are in G Major.

G Major

Exercise 1

Exercise 2

Exercise 3

Scales and arpeggios

C major, to be played from memory

Tone development

1. Ensure maximum flexibility by using a minimum amount of mouthpiece pressure against the lips.
2. Listen carefully to the sound and do not tolerate a pinched, nasal tone quality.
3. Breathe through the corners of the mouth, keeping the embouchure formation as still as possible.
4. Use the rhythm of the exercise to help develop embouchure control.
5. Repeat exercise (a) using the notes shown in exercises (b) (c) (d) and (e).

RIGAUDON

H. Purcell

Allegretto

ALLEMANDE

From a collection of
16th century dances

Allegro

25

UNIT 10

Accent Signs

Dotted Crotchets

An accent sign placed over or under a note means that the note must be given a strong attack with the tongue. Often this strong attack is combined with a little 'punch' from the diaphragm.

Since a dot after a note lengthens that note by half its value, the value of a dotted crotchet will be one and a half crotchet beats; the same length of sound as three quavers added together. Look at the example, then study the similarity of bars 2 and 3 in the first exercise.

Exercise 1

Exercise 2

Exercise 3

THE EMPEROR OF GERMANY'S MARCH

Jeremiah Clarke

Tone development

1. Start with an accent on the first note then use the varying tongue and diaphragm levels to assist the production of the lip-slurs. Vowel shapes similar to those in unit 4 will also help; for downward slurs use 'TEE-OOO-AAA', for upward slurs use 'TAA-OOO-EEE'.

2. Resist any temptation to tongue during the slur; remember that the point of the exercise is to develop a flexible embouchure, not just to produce the notes.

3. Take a small rest after each exercise, but don't move the mouthpiece.

FANFARE

Nicholas Chédeville

27

UNIT 11

A New Note

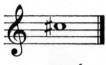

C#

1
2

A New Key-signature

In sharp keys, the name of the major key can be found by counting one letter name up from the last sharp. The example shows a key-signature with two sharps. Since the last sharp is C♯, the name of the major key must be D major.

Accidentals

* *

*Because of the accidental, both these notes are B♭.

When a flat or sharp is used that is not in the key-signature it is called an accidental. An accidental lasts until the next bar-line and because of this, affects any subsequent note of the same pitch in that bar.

Exercise 1

Exercise 2

Frederic Berr

Scales and arpeggios

D Major, to be played from memory

STRUTTIN'

Steve Pogson

Tone development

1. Concentrate on a muscular contraction of the embouchure for playing these smaller interval lip-slurs.
2. Use bars 1 and 2 to establish the muscular feel of the exercise.
3. Play bar 3 at a speed comfortable to your embouchure development.
4. Repeat exercise (a) using the notes shown in exercises (b) (c) and (d).

ALLEGRETTO

Cornelius Gurlitt

CRADLE SONG

J. Brahms

UNIT 12

Natural Signs

Italian Terms

pp   very soft   **ff**   very loud

p   soft   **f**   loud

mp   moderately soft   **mf**   moderately loud

———————— gradually softer   ———————— gradually louder

A natural sign is used to cancel a flat or sharp. Since it is a type of accidental, it will only last for the bar in which it is printed. However, if a note that has been altered occurs again in the next bar, an additional accidental is often used to confirm that the note has returned to its original pitch.

Italian terms also describe the mood of a piece, changes of mood and large repeats such as da capo. As with Italian terms introduced earlier, English translations can be found at the end of the book.

A table of Italian terms which show how loud or soft the music should sound is printed above. It should be used in conjunction with the tuning technique introduced in this unit.

Exercise 1

Exercise 2

J. Arban

Scales and arpeggios:

D Minor (harmonic form) to be played from memory.

TRUMPET AIR

D. Purcell

Moderato

Musicianship

Crescendos and diminuendos play an important part in creating expression but need careful use since they also have an effect on tuning. Basically, a crescendo (produced by increasing the air pressure) will make a note go sharp, and a diminuendo (produced by reducing the air pressure) will make a note go flat.

To stabilise the tuning, allow the lip aperture to open slightly during a crescendo, and close slightly during a diminuendo.

MINUET

Esprit Chédeville

Allegretto

31

UNIT 13

New Notes

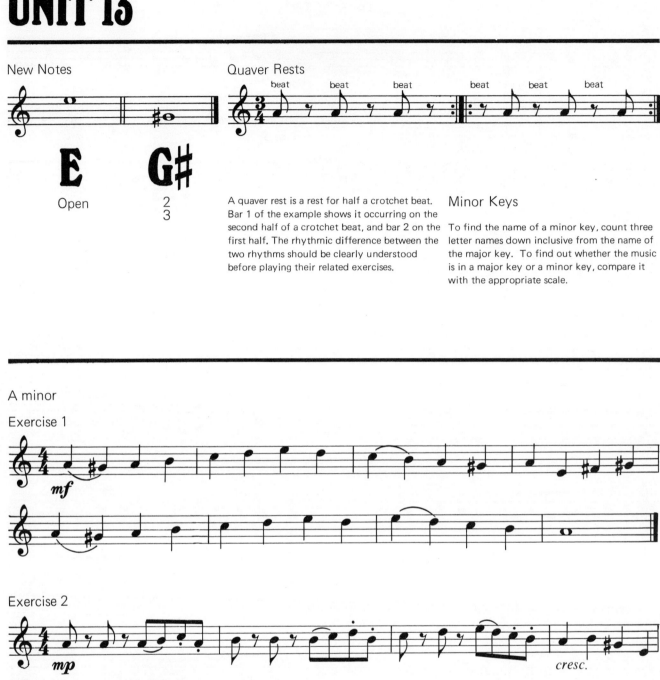

E — Open

G♯ — 2 3

Quaver Rests

beat beat beat beat beat beat

A quaver rest is a rest for half a crotchet beat. Bar 1 of the example shows it occurring on the second half of a crotchet beat, and bar 2 on the first half. The rhythmic difference between the two rhythms should be clearly understood before playing their related exercises.

Minor Keys

To find the name of a minor key, count three letter names down inclusive from the name of the major key. To find out whether the music is in a major key or a minor key, compare it with the appropriate scale.

A minor

Exercise 1

mf

Exercise 2

mp

cresc.

mf

Exercise 3

mp

cresc.

mf

Scales and arpeggios:

A Minor (harmonic form) to be played from memory.

Tone development

1. Start with a small accent, then concentrate on controlling the diminuendo.
2. Keep as still as possible during the first rest.
3. Commence bar 3 with an embouchure formation identical to that formed at the end of bar 1.
4. Remember: diaphragm, minimum mouthpiece pressure, mental awareness of the tiny muscles at the lip centre; these are the control points for expressive playing.
5. Repeat exercise (a) using the notes shown in (b) (c) (d) and (e).

ETUDE

Antonio Diabelli

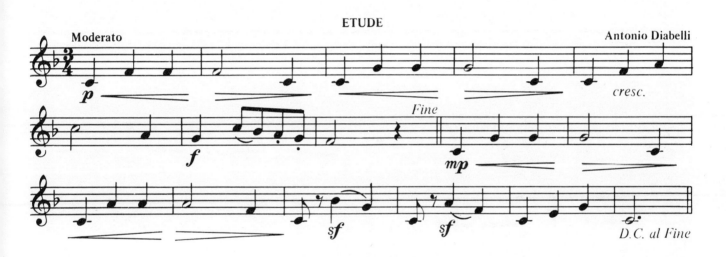

COVENTRY CAROL

An English 16th century carol

UNIT 14

Compound Time

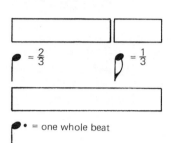

♩ = ⅔ ♪ = ⅓

♩. = one whole beat

Compound Time-signatures

When the natural pulse of a piece divides itself into thirds of a beat, the music is said to be in compound time. The various notes retain the same value in relation to each other; for instance there are still two quavers in a crotchet, but their value in relation to the beat is changed to the values shown in the example.

To show the new note values, a new set of time-signatures is used. The example shows six-eight, indicating two dotted crotchet beats in a bar. A chart showing the complete range of compound time-signatures and how they are applied is printed at the end of the book.

Exercise 1

Exercise 2

Exercise 3

MARMOTTE

L. van Beethoven

Aids to music reading

When reading notes which are thirds of a beat, read them as if they were three-syllable words. As an example of this, try the first exercise thinking the word TENTATIVE as you play each group. When playing the pieces, apply this reading principle to all rhythmic groups contained within one beat.

DUETTO

Adapted from a duet
by D. Gatti

UNIT 15

New Notes

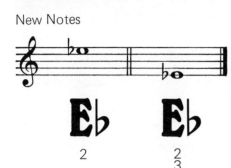

Double Names for Notes

A♯ = B♭   C♯ = D♭   D♯ = E♭   F♯ = G♭   G♯ = A♭

The interval between A and B is one whole tone. Since a sharp raises a note by half a tone, and a flat lowers a note by half a tone, it follows that A♯ and B♭ are different names for the same note. Double names can be given to all the flats and sharps learned so far.

A New Key-signature

In flat keys, the name of the major key can be found by counting four letter names down from the last flat. The key-signature of exercise 1 has B♭ and E♭, therefore the name of the major key is B♭ Major.

Exercise 1

Exercise 2

Exercise 3

36

Scales and arpeggios

E Minor (harmonic form) to be played from memory.

Tone development

1. Start with a small accent, then carefully follow the dynamics.
2. Produce the second note by choosing just the right amount of controlled physical relaxation.

3. Remember that rests between the exercises are almost as important as the exercises themselves.
4. Repeat exercise (a) using the notes shown in exercises (b) (c) (d) (e) and (f).

A LITTLE PIECE

Moderato

Antonio Diabelli

A MELODY IN PHRYGIAN MODE
No. 28 from "Mikrokosmos" Vol.1

Béla Bartók

Allegretto

UNIT 16

Tenuto Signs

1st and 2nd time bars

A tenuto sign placed over or under a note means that the note is to be played with a lingering pressure. Usually it is also associated with a type of tonguing where one syllable is added to another without any noticeable break in the air stream.

Sometimes the ending of a repeated section is altered the second time through. When this occurs, 1st and 2nd time bars are used. The example is taken from ''Ein' feste Burg'' in

which bars 1 - 4 are played quite normally the first time through, but when they are repeated the first time bar is omitted and the second time bar played instead.

Exercise 1

Exercise 2

Exercise 3

EIN' FESTE BURG

A chorale by M. Luther
adapted by J. S. Bach

Musicianship

Sometimes the general character of a piece suggests that many of the notes should be played staccato. When this occurs, the dots on top of the notes are often omitted, leaving it to the instrumentalist to interpret the music in a staccato style. The "Duo" by Chédeville is an example of this.

DUO IN G MINOR

Esprit Chédeville

CONCERT PIECES FOR UNITS 9-16

As with earlier concert pieces, piano accompaniments should be used to provide experience in playing with an accompanist. 'Two Trumpet Airs' by Lully is an example of music that has been set for early grade examinations.

TWO TRUMPET AIRS
from "Xerxes"

J. B. LULLY
(1632-1687)
arr. PETER WASTALL

© Copyright 1979 by Boosey & Hawkes Music Publishers Ltd.

SOLILOQUY

DEREK HYDE

© Copyright 1979 by Boosey & Hawkes Music Publishers Ltd.

MIDNIGHT IN TOBAGO

Tempo di tango

PETER WASTALL

UNIT 17

A New Note

F

1

Grace Notes

In their simplest form, grace notes are notes added to a melody to make the music sound more decorative. To show how they are used, first play the example without the pair of grace notes, then again, using the grace notes to decorate the second A. As a general rule, grace notes should be played gracefully and lightly.

STUDY No. 1
from 'Method for the Cornet', op.13

Pierre Clodomir

ON WINGS OF SONG

F. Mendelssohn

Andante tranquillo

Tone development

1. Use these exercises to continue the development of tongue and diaphragm co-ordination.
2. For downward slurs (notes 2 and 4), form an 'AAA' syllable and enlarge the mouth cavity by slightly opening the gap between the teeth.

3. For upward slurs (notes 3 and 5) help the embouchure contraction by forming either an 'OOO' syllable or an 'EEE' syllable, depending on the pitch of the note.
4. As before, repeat exercise (a) using the fingerings indicated.

MARCH

G. F. Handel

Maestoso

UNIT 18

Semiquavers

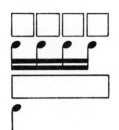

Syncopation

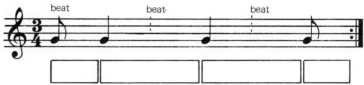

The value of a semiquaver is a quarter of a crotchet; it is printed with two tails on the end of its stem. As with quavers, all the tails contained in one beat can be joined together.

A new rhythm, called syncopation, is produced when strongly accented notes occur between the beats instead of coinciding with them.

As shown in the duet, the surrounding quavers are usually played staccato to help bounce the syncopated notes off the beat.

Exercise 1

Exercise 2

Scales and arpeggios:

F Major, to be played from memory.

AN OLD HUNGARIAN DANCE

P. Károlyi
(b.1934)

Aids to music reading

With blocks of four semiquavers, read each group as you would a four-syllable word. Start with passages that are easy to play (such as the two exercises shown opposite) and make a conscious effort to read each block of four semiquavers as a single unit.

A SYNCOPATED DUET

François Garnier

UNIT 19

A New Note

Bb

1

Dotted Quavers

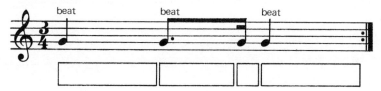

A dotted quaver, or its equivalent rest, lasts for three quarters of a crotchet beat. Usually it is combined with a single semiquaver since this completes the beat.

STUDY No.2
from 'Method for the Cornet', op.13

P. Clodomir

SERENADE

Maestoso

Jeremiah Clarke

Aids to music reading

The reading technique for a single semiquaver is to group the semiquaver with the note which follows. In lively movements, a useful way to achieve this is to pronounce the two notes as if saying the word TODAY. As an example, play the first note of the "Soldier's March" by Schumann, then think TODAY as you play the next two notes. This reading technique can be used every time a dotted rhythm occurs.

SOLDIER'S MARCH

Allegro deciso

R. Schumann

UNIT 20

Semiquaver Rests

Note patterns using Semiquavers

A semiquaver rests is a rest for a quarter of a crotchet beat. Notice that it is similar to the semiquaver note, being printed with two tails. Examples of the semiquaver rest can be found in the duet.

By combining semiquavers with quavers, several new rhythm patterns can be formed. The examples should be studied carefully before playing the exercises.

Exercise 1

Exercise 2

Scales and arpeggios:

B♭ Major, to be played from memory.

SHORE'S TRUMPET TUNE

Pomposo

From an eighteenth century
collection of trumpet tunes

Musicianship

As you play the "Duetto" by Devienne, notice that the general character is one of smoothness. To achieve this smoothness, use a very gentle type of tonguing; rather like pronouncing the syllable DAH. When playing in this manner, we say we are interpreting the music in a legato style. Compare the style with that needed for playing Shore's trumpet tune, where the mood demands that a vigorous, accented type of tonguing be used.

DUETTO

Andante

F. Devienne

UNIT 21

A New Note

C#

1 *
2
3
↓

Three-eight Time

The time-signature of three-eight indicates that there are three quaver beats in each bar. As before, the various notes retain the same value in relation to each other; it is the value of the notes in relation to the beat that is changed.

* Fingering 1-2-3 is very sharp in pitch. Lip down to correct the tuning.

STUDY No.3
from 'Method for the Cornet and Saxhorn', op.14

P. Clodomir

Tone development

1. Give the first note a fairly strong attack, then concentrate on controlling the lip aperture so that the exercise remains in tune.
2. As before, repeat exercise (a) but this time use natural fingering throughout, making sure there are no ungainly bumps.

3. Fingering 1-2-3 is very sharp in pitch. In some passages, this can be corrected by pushing the 3rd valve slide out a little way; however, it is usually more convenient to correct the sharpness by a small relaxation of the lip aperture. Make this adjustment in exercise (f).

UNIT 22

Triplets

Two-two Time

A triplet can be defined as 'three notes played in the time of two notes of the same value' (for instance, three quavers played in the time of two quavers). The number 3 is placed over or under the notes to show the momentary change of note value.

The time-signature of two-two indicates that there are two minim beats in each bar. The value of the notes in relation to the beat is shown in the example. Sometimes two-two is called Alla Breve.

Exercise 1

Exercise 2

Scales and arpeggios:

B♭ Major, to be played from memory.

FANFARE

Allegro vivace

W. A. Mozart

f *ben marcato*

Tone development

1. Descend by relaxation, making sure the facial muscles remain under control.
2. If the lower notes fail to respond, check the pressure of the mouthpiece against the lips, remember, for lower tones the bottom lip in particular must be free to vibrate.
3. If a note fails to 'speak' in the ascending slur, resist the temptation to tongue it; instead, take a small rest then try the exercise one semitone lower.
4. Repeat exercise (a) using the notes shown in exercises (b) (c) and (d).

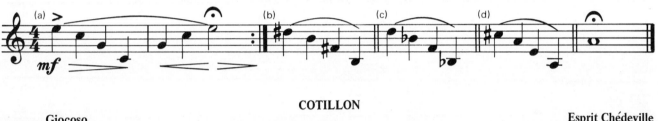

COTILLON

Giocoso

Esprit Chédeville

UNIT 23

New Notes

Change of Time-signature

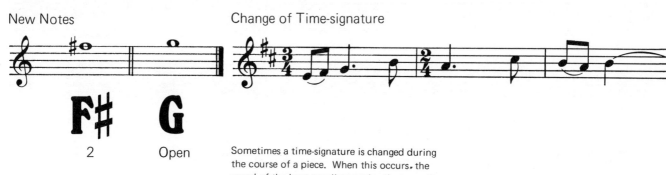

F#   **G**

2   Open

Sometimes a time-signature is changed during the course of a piece. When this occurs, the speed of the beat usually remains the same; it is the pulse pattern that changes. The example is taken from the "Cantilene" by Árpad Balázs.

STUDY No.4

from 'Method for the Cornet', op.13

P. Clodomir

CANTILENA
from "Piano Miniatures for Children"

Árpád Balázs
(b. 1937)

Tone development

1. Use the first note to check and establish the embouchure formation.
2. Start the lip-slur with a 'TOOO' syllable, then use relaxation and a slightly lower tongue-level to produce the second note.
3. For notes 3 and 5, raise the tongue-level, making sure the diaphragm is giving co-ordinated support.
4. Repeat exercise (a) through each valve combination, starting on the notes shown.

ALMANDE

Giles Farnaby

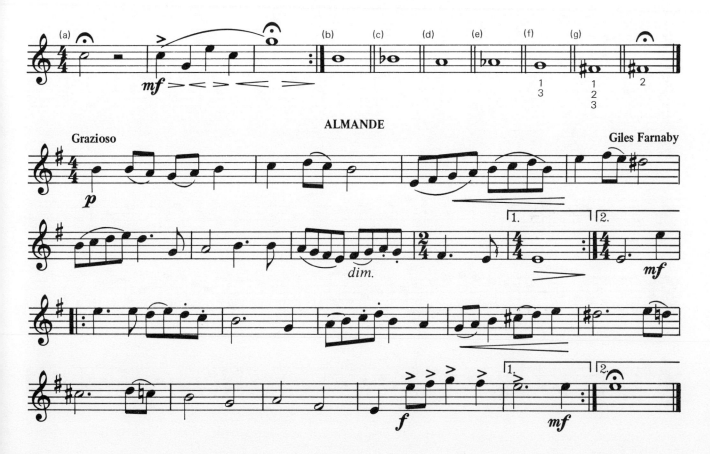

UNIT 24

Acciaccaturas

Rests of Several Bars

An acciaccatura is a small grace note with a stroke through its stem. It should be played on the beat and as short as possible.

When a rest of several bars is required, only one bar is used; a black line is usually drawn in this bar, and the number of complete bars to be counted placed on top. The example is taken from the final section of the concert piece on p. 61.

Exercise 1

J. B. Arban

mf *ben marcato*

cresc.

mp

f

Scales and arpeggios:

G Major, to be played from memory.

C Major, to be played from memory

E Major, to be played from memory.

ANDANTE — Andante — Antonio Diabelli

Musicianship

Both pieces in this unit have performing directions relating to their mood: the "Andante" by Diabelli is marked dolce espressivo, and the Charpentier "Fanfare" con bravura. As you practise, try to create these moods using the appropriate staccato and legato styles of playing. In the "Andante", the shapes of the phrases create good opportunities for displaying control over the dynamics; the important thing to remember is that performing directions are the starting point for creating your own expression.

FANFARE — Vivace — M. A. Charpentier

CONCERT PIECES FOR UNITS 17-24

'March' by Handel and 'Serenade' by Grètry
are examples of music that have been set for
early grade examinations.

MARCH
from "Scipio"

G. F. HANDEL
(1685-1759)
arr. PETER WASTALL

A GAME OF TAG
from "Trumpet Music for Beginners"

JÓZSEF KARAI
(b. 1927)

SERENADE

from "L'Amant Jaloux"

ANDRÉ GRÉTRY
(1741-1813)
arr. PETER WASTALL

PRELUDE
from "Te Deum"

M. A. CHARPENTIER
(1634-1704)
arr. PETER WASTALL

SUBURBAN SUNDAY

KEITH RAMON COLE

BASIC FINGERING CHART

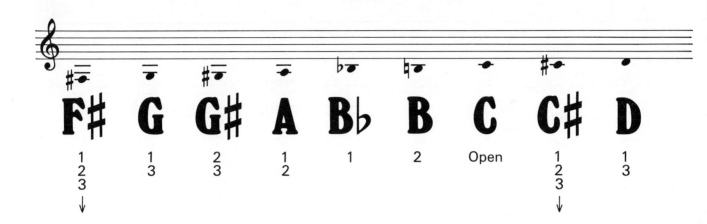

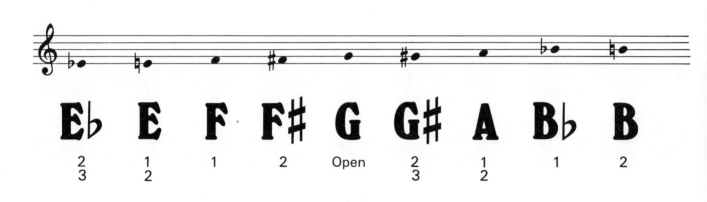

↓ Lip down to correct the tuning. (See Unit
21 for detailed tehnique)

A   B♭   B   C

1   1   2   Open
2

Notes available from each valve combination

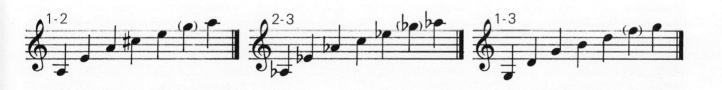

The trumpet, cornet and flugel horn are
transposing instruments and sound as
follows:

written   sounds

TIME SIGNATURES

1. Look up the time signature

2. Look in the left hand column to find the number of beats in each bar.

3. Look in the top row above the time signature to find the type of note that equals one beat.

	Simple time			Compound time		
Value of each beat (type of note)	𝅗𝅥	♩	♪	𝅗𝅥.	♩.	♪.
Value of each beat as a fraction of a semibreve	$\frac{1}{2}$	$\frac{1}{4}$	$\frac{1}{8}$	$\frac{3}{4}$	$\frac{3}{8}$	$\frac{3}{16}$
2 beats in each bar	$\frac{2}{2}$	$\frac{2}{4}$	$\frac{2}{8}$	$\frac{6}{4}$	$\frac{6}{8}$	$\frac{6}{16}$
3 beats in each bar	$\frac{3}{2}$	$\frac{3}{4}$	$\frac{3}{8}$	$\frac{9}{4}$	$\frac{9}{8}$	$\frac{9}{16}$
4 beats in each bar	$\frac{4}{2}$	$\frac{4}{4}$	$\frac{4}{8}$	$\frac{12}{4}$	$\frac{12}{8}$	$\frac{12}{16}$

ITALIAN TERMS

A tempo Resume the normal speed.
Accelerando Becoming gradually faster.
Adagio Slow, leisurely.
Agitato Agitated.
Alla marcia In the style of a march.
Allargando Broadening out.
Allegretto Slightly slower than Allegro.
Allegro Lively, reasonably fast.
Andante (lit. walking) At a moderate pace.
Andantino A little andante.
Animato Animated.
Cantabile In a singing style.
Con With.
Crescendo *(cresc.)* Becoming louder.
Da Capo (D.C.) al Fine Back to the beginning and finish at the word Fine.
Dal Segno (D. S.) From the sign 𝄋
Deciso Decisively, firmly.
Diminuendo *(dim.)* Becoming gradually softer.
Dolce Sweetly.

E, Ed And.
Espressivo *(espress.)* With expression, with feeling.
Forte (*f*) Loud.
Fortissimo (*ff*) Very loud.
Giocoso Humorously.
Grazioso Gracefully.
Largo Slow and stately, broad.
Larghetto Less slow than Largo.
Legato Smoothly.
Leggiero Lightly.
Lento Slowly.
Maestoso Majestically.
Meno mosso Less movement.
Mezzo forte (*mf*) Moderately loud.
Mezzo piano (*mp*) Moderately soft.
Moderato Moderate time.
Molto Much.
Moto Movement.
Non troppo Not too much.
Pianissimo (*pp*) Very soft.

Piano (*p*) Soft.
Più mosso More movement, quicker.
Poco a poco Little by little (gradually).
Pomposo Pompously.
Presto Very quick.
Quasi As if, almost.
Rallentando (rall.) Becoming gradually slower.
Ritenuto (rit.) Hold back (slower at once).
Rubato Flexibly.
Semplice Simple.
Sempre Always.
Sforzando (*sf* , *sfz*) Forcing, accented.
Solenne Solemn.
Sonore Sonorous, full toned.
Sostenuto Sustained.
Spirito Spirit, life, energy.
Tempo I Resume the original speed.
Tenuto Held.
Tranquillo Quietly.
Un poco A little.
Vivace Lively, quick.

Printed by
Halstan & Co. Ltd., Amersham, Bucks., England